W9-BLT-233

Practice for **FIVE** types of writing...

- Personal narrative
- Story writing
- Descriptive writing
- Letters
- Simple instructions

Written by Kim Minafo

Managing Editor: Hope Taylor Spencer

Editorial Team: Becky S. Andrews, Kimberley Bruck, Sharon Murphy, Debra Liverman, Diane Badden, Thad H. McLaurin, Jennifer Bragg, Karen A. Brudnak, Hope Rodgers, Dorothy C. McKinney

Production Team: Lori Z. Henry, Pam Crane, Rebecca Saunders, Chris Curry, Sarah Foreman, Theresa Lewis Goode, Greg D. Rieves, Eliseo De Jesus Santos II, Barry Slate, Donna K. Teal, Zane Williard, Tazmen Carlisle, Kathy Coop, Marsha Heim, Lynette Dickerson, Mark Rainey, Amy Kirtley-Hill

76 Reproducible Writing Activities

www.themailbox.com

©2007 The Mailbox®
All rights reserved.
ISBN10 #1-56234-768-3 • ISBN13 #978-156234-768-0

Manufactured in the United States
10 9 8 7 6 5 4 3 2 1

Table of Contents

What's Inside

76 REPRODUCIBLE WRITING ACTIVITIES

for independent work, center work, small-group work, and homework!

ENGAGING PROMPT

SKILL LINE SHOWING THE TYPE OF WRITING

PREWRITING ORGANIZER TO HELP STUDENTS PLAN

WRITING TASK

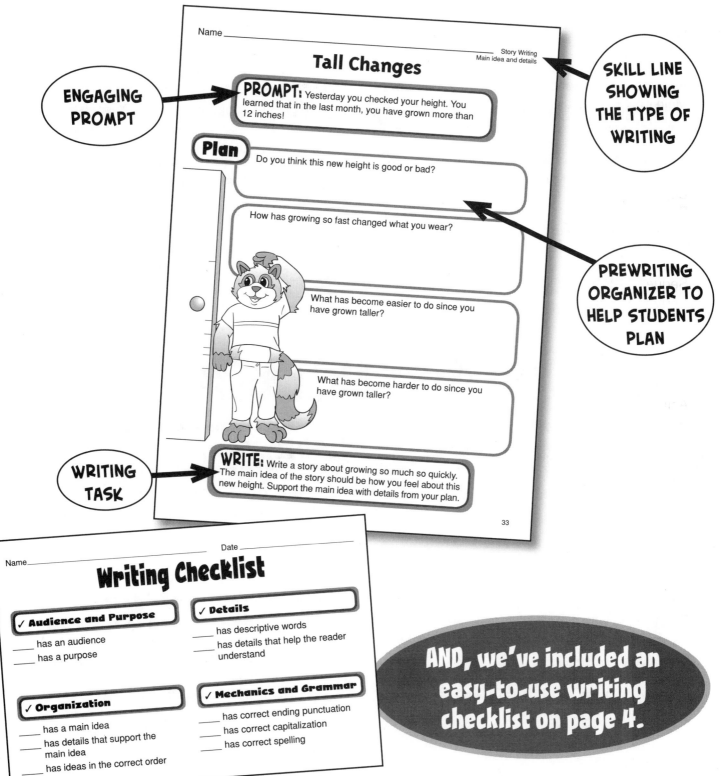

Name _____

Story Writing
Main idea and details

Tall Changes

PROMPT: Yesterday you checked your height. You learned that in the last month, you have grown more than 12 inches!

Plan

Do you think this new height is good or bad?

How has growing so fast changed what you wear?

What has become easier to do since you have grown taller?

What has become harder to do since you have grown taller?

WRITE: Write a story about growing so much so quickly. The main idea of the story should be how you feel about this new height. Support the main idea with details from your plan.

33

Name _____ Date _____

Writing Checklist

✓ Audience and Purpose
___ has an audience
___ has a purpose

✓ Organization
___ has a main idea
___ has details that support the main idea
___ has ideas in the correct order

✓ Details
___ has descriptive words
___ has details that help the reader understand

✓ Mechanics and Grammar
___ has correct ending punctuation
___ has correct capitalization
___ has correct spelling

AND, we've included an easy-to-use writing checklist on page 4.

Name —————————————————— Date ——————————————————

Writing Checklist

✓ Audience and Purpose

_____ has an audience
_____ has a purpose

✓ Details

_____ has descriptive words
_____ has details that help the reader understand

✓ Organization

_____ has a main idea
_____ has details that support the main idea
_____ has ideas in the correct order

✓ Mechanics and Grammar

_____ has correct ending punctuation
_____ has correct capitalization
_____ has correct spelling

– –

Name —————————————————— Date ——————————————————

Writing Checklist

✓ Audience and Purpose

_____ has an audience
_____ has a purpose

✓ Details

_____ has descriptive words
_____ has details that help the reader understand

✓ Organization

_____ has a main idea
_____ has details that support the main idea
_____ has ideas in the correct order

✓ Mechanics and Grammar

_____ has correct ending punctuation
_____ has correct capitalization
_____ has correct spelling

Name_____

Brrrr...It's Cold!

Prompt: Think about a time when you were very cold.

Plan

Where were you?

What were you wearing?

Why were you so cold?

How did you get warm?

Write: Write about a time when you were very cold. Help the reader understand the event by setting the scene and then describing what happened.

Name_____

Where Did It Go?

Prompt: Think about a time when you lost something that was important to you.

Plan

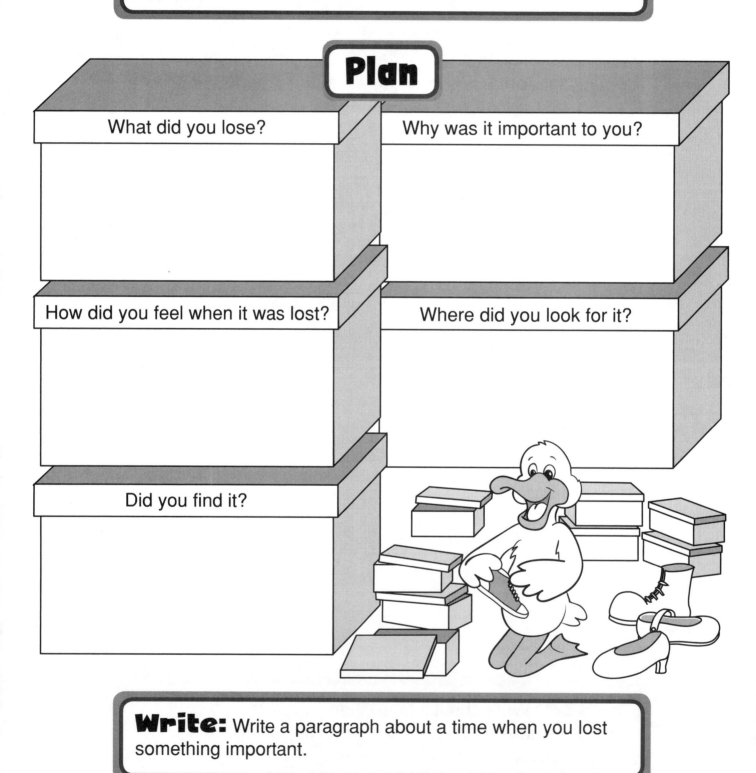

What did you lose?

Why was it important to you?

How did you feel when it was lost?

Where did you look for it?

Did you find it?

Write: Write a paragraph about a time when you lost something important.

Family Practice

Prompt: A tradition is a custom or routine that has been handed down through a family. Think about your favorite tradition that your family shares.

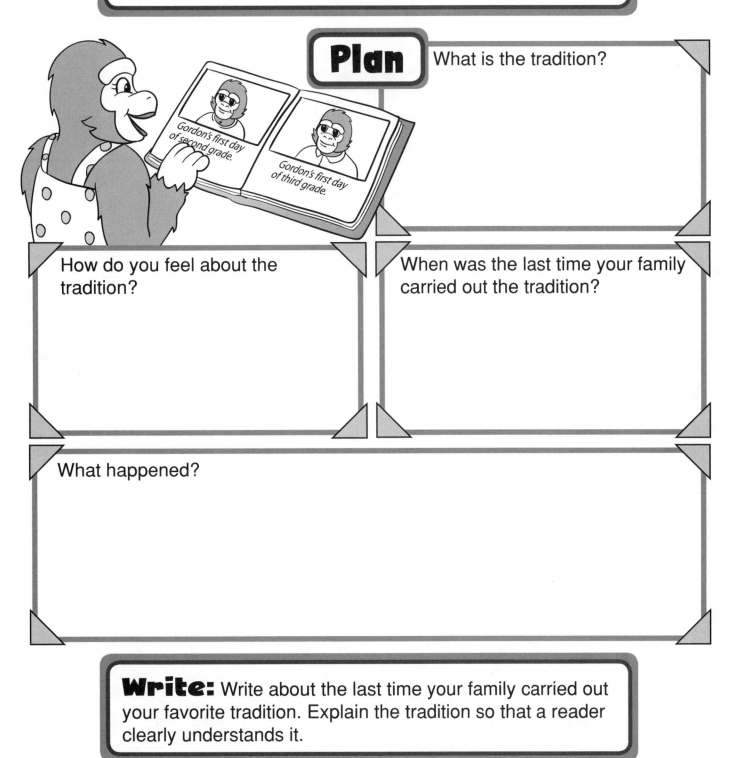

Plan

What is the tradition?

How do you feel about the tradition?

When was the last time your family carried out the tradition?

What happened?

Write: Write about the last time your family carried out your favorite tradition. Explain the tradition so that a reader clearly understands it.

I'm the Star!

Prompt: Everyone has the chance to shine at some time. Think about a time when you were a star.

Plan

Where were you?

Who was there?

What were you doing?

How did you feel?

Write: Write about the time when you felt like a star.

A Thrill in the Air

Prompt: What is the most exciting event that happened at school this year?

Plan

When did the event happen?

Where did the event happen?

Who was a part of the event?

What happened?

Why was the event so exciting?

Write: Write a paragraph to read to someone at home. Tell about the most exciting event that happened at school this year.

Construction Site

Prompt: Blocks, wood, and even playing cards can each be used for building. Think about something you have recently built.

Plan

What did you build?

What did you use to build it?

Why were you building it?

How did you feel when you were finished?

Write: Write a paragraph for a school newsletter. Describe what you built and why you built it.

A Bad Day

Prompt: It's not fun when things don't go your way!
Think about a day when everything seemed to go wrong.

Plan

What happened?

How did you feel?

What could you do to keep this from happening again?

Write: Write about a bad day that you had. Use details to help the reader understand why it was bad.

Time With a Friend

Prompt: Think about time you spend with a pet.

Plan

What kind of pet is it?

What is the pet's name?

How do you feel about this pet?

What did the pet do to make you feel this way?

Write: Write a paragraph telling about time you spend with the pet. Use your feelings about the pet as your main idea. Support your main idea with details telling why you feel this way.

Name _____

Job Well Done

Prompt: Think about a time when someone was proud of you.

Plan

Who was proud of you?

What did you do that made this person proud?

How did you know this person was proud of you?

How did this make you feel?

Write: Write a paragraph describing a time when you made someone proud of you. Support your main idea with important details.

Name

Hard at Work

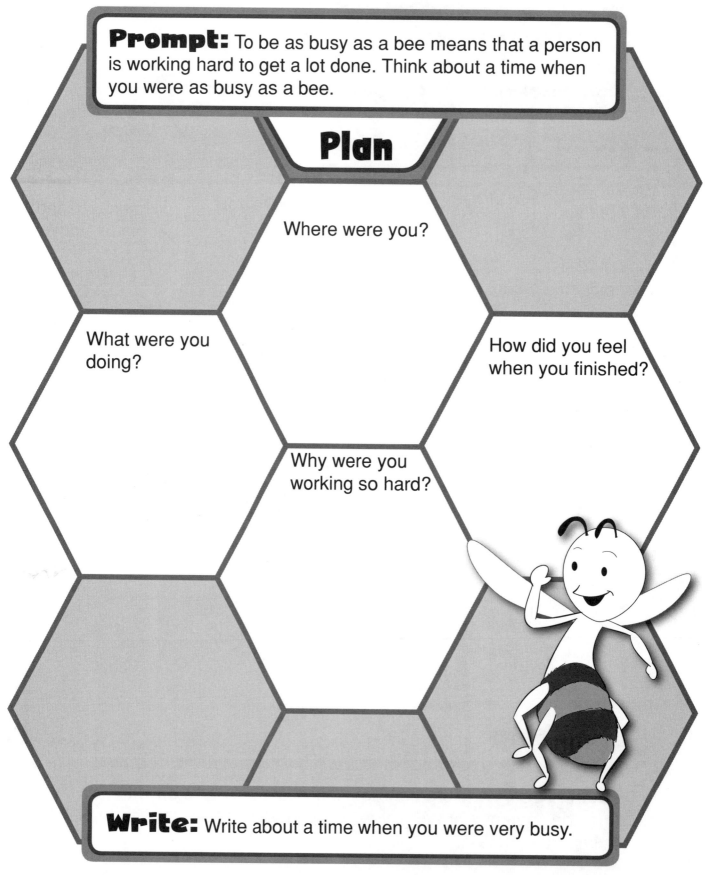

Prompt: To be as busy as a bee means that a person is working hard to get a lot done. Think about a time when you were as busy as a bee.

Plan

Where were you?

What were you doing?

How did you feel when you finished?

Why were you working so hard?

Write: Write about a time when you were very busy.

Going the Distance

Prompt: People can travel by taking cars, planes, or trains. Think about a time when you traveled a long distance.

Plan

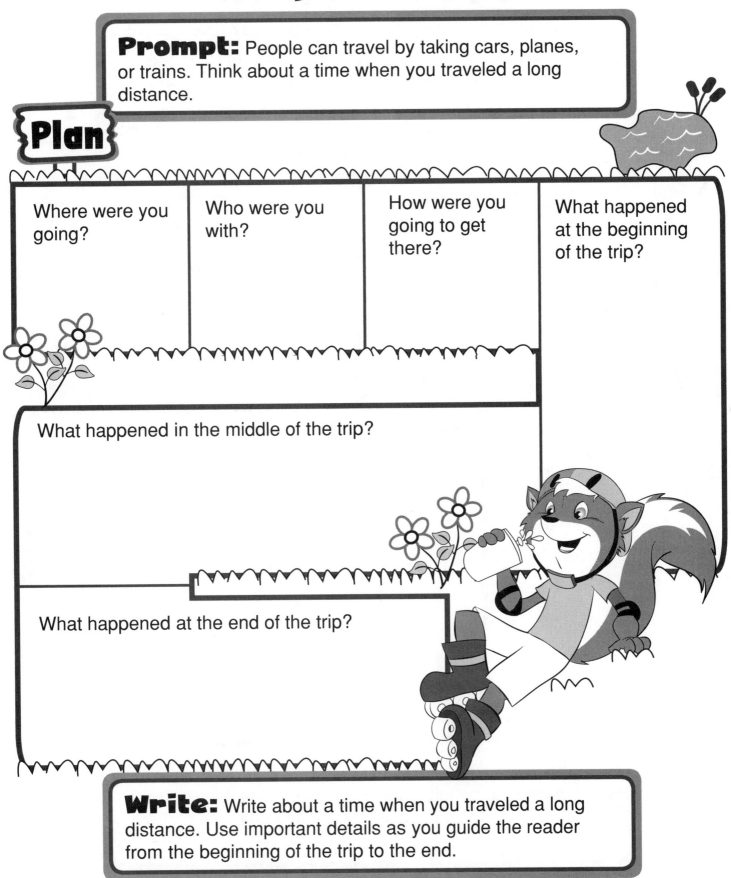

Where were you going?

Who were you with?

How were you going to get there?

What happened at the beginning of the trip?

What happened in the middle of the trip?

What happened at the end of the trip?

Write: Write about a time when you traveled a long distance. Use important details as you guide the reader from the beginning of the trip to the end.

A Good Time After All

Prompt: Sometimes an activity turns out to be fun, even though you weren't expecting it to be at first. Think about a time you had fun when you didn't expect to.

Plan

Where were you?

Who were you with?

What happened at the beginning of the activity?

What happened in the middle of the activity?

What happened at the end of the activity?

Write: Write about a time when you thought an activity was not going to be fun, but it was. Use words to help the reader understand your feelings from the beginning of the activity to the end.

Practice Makes Perfect?

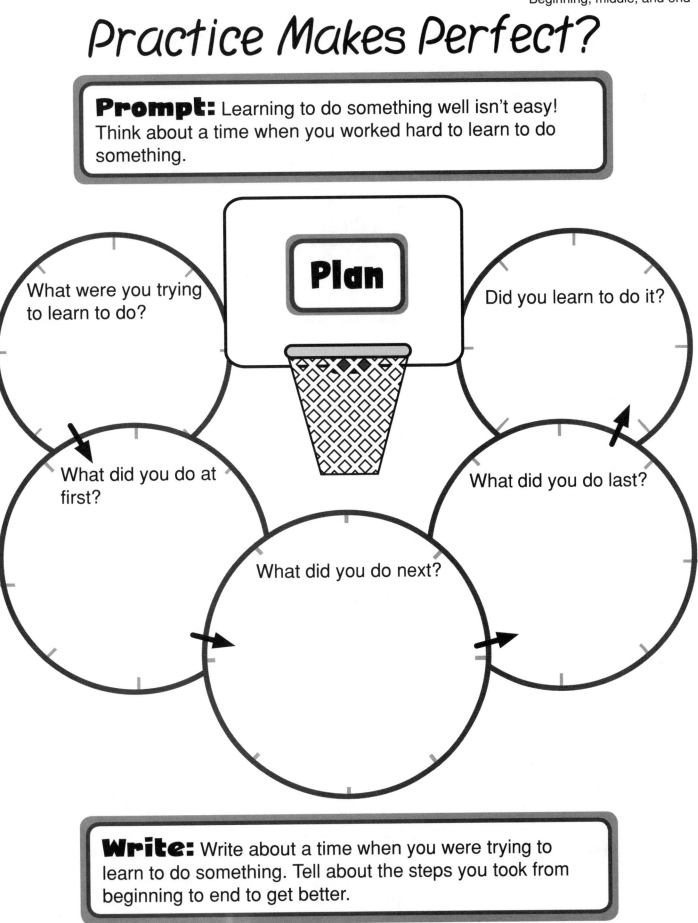

Prompt: Learning to do something well isn't easy! Think about a time when you worked hard to learn to do something.

Plan

What were you trying to learn to do?

Did you learn to do it?

What did you do at first?

What did you do last?

What did you do next?

Write: Write about a time when you were trying to learn to do something. Tell about the steps you took from beginning to end to get better.

A Memorable Meeting

Prompt: Insects can be interesting! They can also be pests. Think about an encounter you have had with an insect.

Plan

Where were you?

What kind of insect was it?

How did the encounter begin?

What happened next?

How did the encounter end?

Write: Write about an encounter you've had with an insect from beginning to end.

In Good Hands

Prompt: Some things have to be handled with care. Some people do too. Think about a time when you had to be extra careful with something or someone.

Plan

What or who were you treating carefully?

What are four things you did to show that you were careful?

Why did you have to be careful?

Write: Write about a time when you had to be extra careful with something or someone.

Peas in a Pod

Prompt: Think about a fun day you spent with one or more good friends. What happened?

Plan

How did your day begin?

What was the most fun thing you did all day?

What other fun things did you do?

How did this day end?

Write: Write about your day. Tell about the important events in the order they happened.

A Special Guest

Prompt: When was the last time you were a guest at someone's home?

Plan

Who were you visiting?

Why were you visiting?

What happened during the visit?

First,

Next,

Then,

Finally,

Write: Write about the last time you were a guest.
Retell the events of your visit in the order they happened.

A Big Step

Prompt: Trying something new can be fun! Think about a time when you tried something new.

Plan

What did you try?

What did you do first?

Then what happened?

How did it turn out?

What happened next?

Write: Write about a time when you tried something new. Describe the event from start to finish.

Imagine That!

Prompt: Is your favorite dream (or daydream) funny, scary, or full of adventure?

What is your dream about?

Plan

What do you see in your dream?

What do you hear in your dream?

How does your dream make you feel?

Write: Write about your favorite dream (or daydream). Use describing words that will help a reader understand what you see, hear, and feel in your dream.

Good Times

Prompt: To be as happy as a clam means to be very happy. Think about a time when you were as happy as a clam.

Plan

Where were you?

What were you doing?

Why did you feel so happy?

What other words describe how you felt?

Write: Write a paragraph about the time when you were as happy as a clam. Be sure to describe what made you happy and how happy you were.

The Big Winners

Prompt: Think about a time when you played a game.

What game did you play?

Where did you play?

Who else played?

How did you feel during the game?

Who won the game?

How did you feel when it was over?

Plan

Write: Write about a time when you played a game.

Lending a Hand

Prompt: A baby bird has fallen from its nest. The nest is too high for you to return the bird, so you bring it home with you. You decide to take care of it until it can fly.

Plan

What do you feed the bird?

How do you feed the bird?

How do you keep the bird warm?

How do you keep the bird safe?

How do you help the bird become a better flier?

Write: Write a story about helping a baby bird. Use what you know about birds to make your story sound as if it could be true.

Life at the Top

Prompt: Crash! Boom! You are a heavy, gray storm cloud in the sky. Think about your life.

Plan

What are you made of?

How did you form?

What kind of weather do you bring?

Do you work alone, or do you have help?

Write: Write a story about your life as a storm cloud. Use details from your plan to help you.

World Traveler

Prompt: Ocean waters carry shells from place to place. Pretend that you are a shell that has washed up on the beach after a long ocean journey.

Plan

Where did your journey start?

When did it start?

What was the ocean like during your journey?

What do you think of the place where you have landed?

Will you stay here, or will you continue to travel?

Write: Write a story about being a shell that has taken a long trip in the ocean.

Your Royal Highness

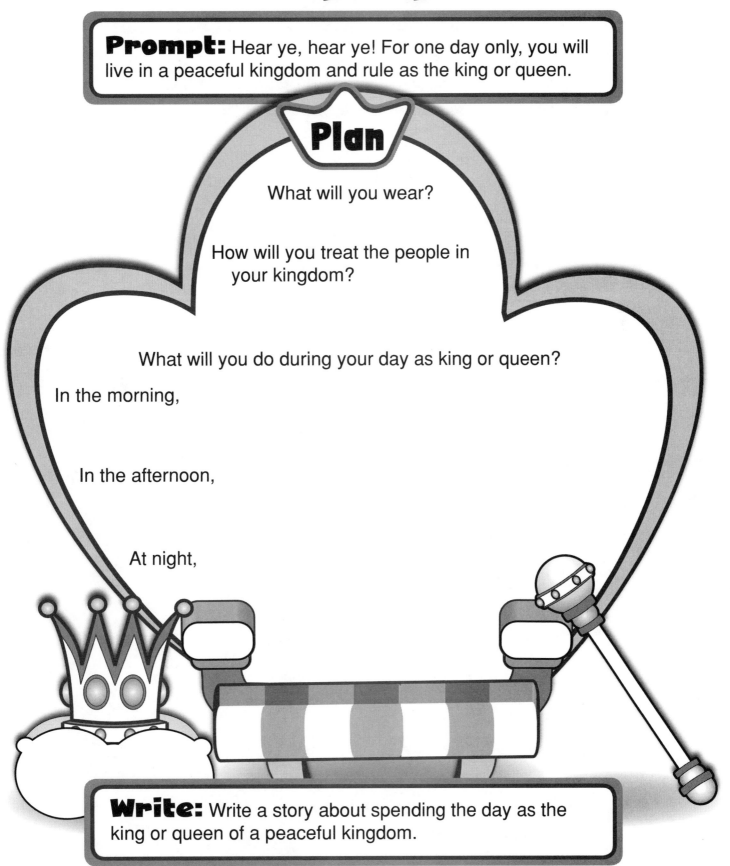

Prompt: Hear ye, hear ye! For one day only, you will live in a peaceful kingdom and rule as the king or queen.

Plan

What will you wear?

How will you treat the people in your kingdom?

What will you do during your day as king or queen?

In the morning,

In the afternoon,

At night,

Write: Write a story about spending the day as the king or queen of a peaceful kingdom.

Special Slumber Party

Prompt: Guess who is having a sleepover? You are! And you are allowed to invite any three people you choose!

Whom will you invite?

When will you have your sleepover?

Plan

What will you and your guests do at your sleepover?

What will you and your guests eat?

Write: Write a story about having a sleepover. Use your plan to guide your story.

Under the Big Top

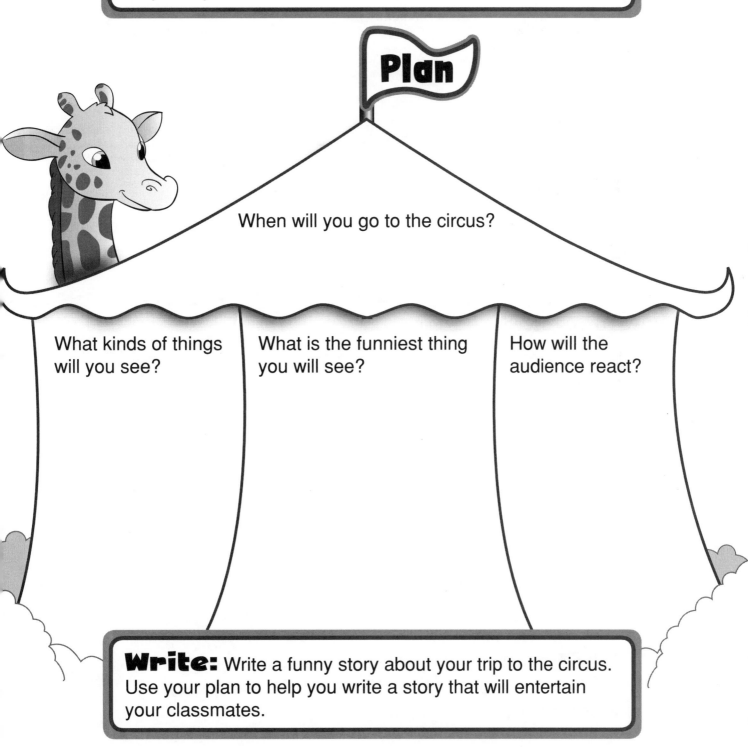

Prompt: There are many things to see at the circus. There are clowns and animals from all over the world. Imagine that you are going to the circus, to see something very funny.

Plan

When will you go to the circus?

What kinds of things will you see?

What is the funniest thing you will see?

How will the audience react?

Write: Write a funny story about your trip to the circus. Use your plan to help you write a story that will entertain your classmates.

Name _____

That's Some Seed!

Prompt: It's your lucky day! You have found a magic seed. When you plant it, it grows something every kid wants.

Plan

What grows from the seed?

Why is this thing important to kids?

How would kids describe this thing?

How much money do you think kids would pay for this thing?

Write: Write a story about a magic seed. Tell what the seed grows and include details to explain why it is important.

Tall Changes

Prompt: Yesterday you checked your height. You learned that in the last month, you have grown more than 12 inches!

Plan

Do you think this new height is good or bad?

How has growing so fast changed what you wear?

What has become easier to do since you have grown taller?

What has become harder to do since you have grown taller?

Write: Write a story about growing so much so quickly. The main idea of the story should be how you feel about this new height. Support the main idea with details from your plan.

Missing Mitt

Prompt: You are a baseball mitt that has been left at the field after a game.

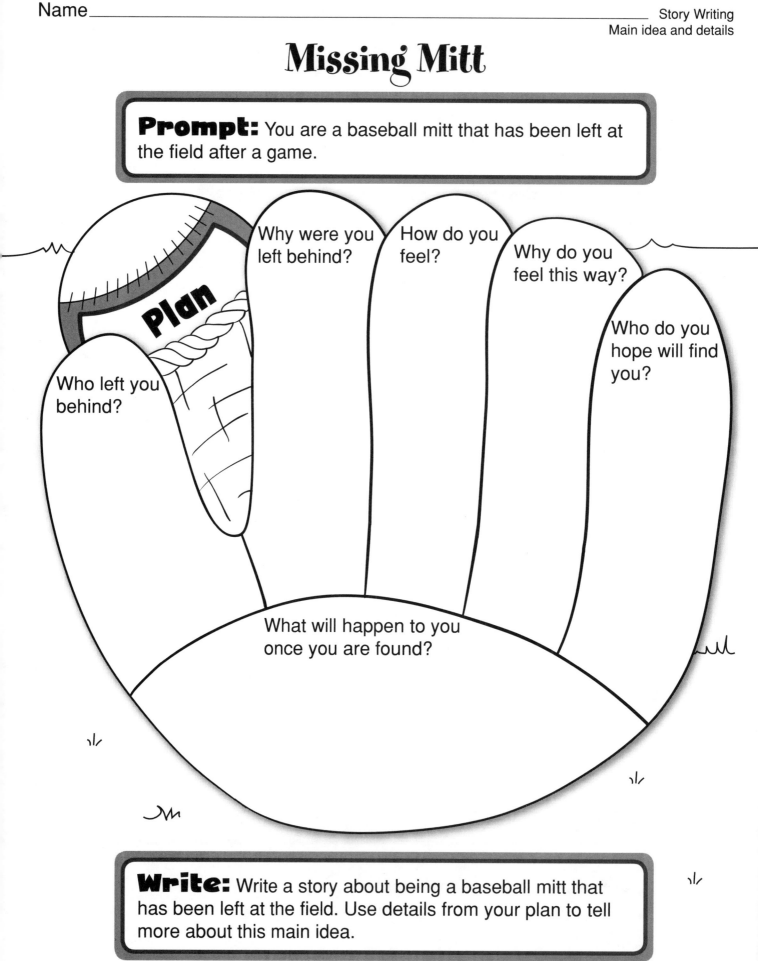

Plan

Who left you behind?

Why were you left behind?

How do you feel?

Why do you feel this way?

Who do you hope will find you?

What will happen to you once you are found?

Write: Write a story about being a baseball mitt that has been left at the field. Use details from your plan to tell more about this main idea.

Student Teacher

Prompt: Your teacher is out for the day, and you have been put in charge of your class!

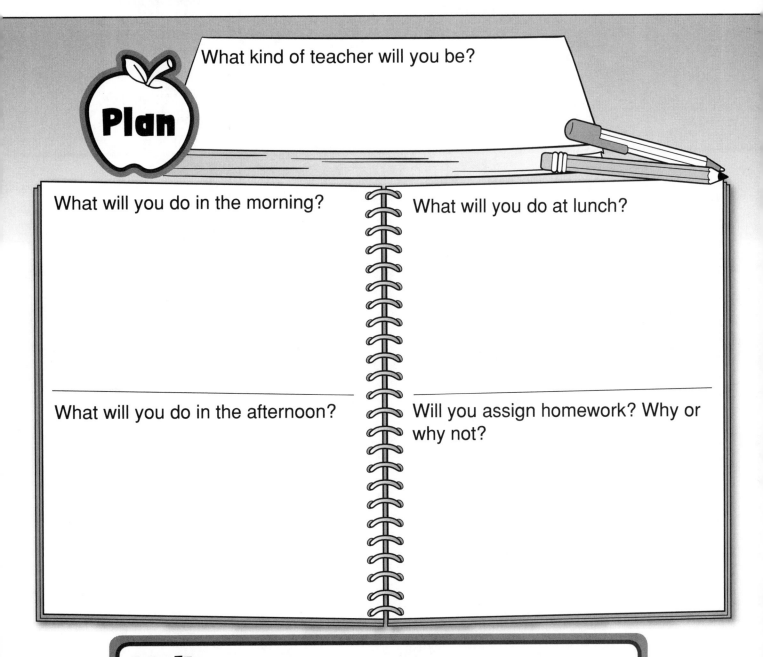

Plan

What kind of teacher will you be?

What will you do in the morning?

What will you do at lunch?

What will you do in the afternoon?

Will you assign homework? Why or why not?

Write: Write a story about being in charge of your class for a day. The main idea of your story should be what kind of teacher you will be. Use details to prove you will be that way.

Name_____

Setback at Sea

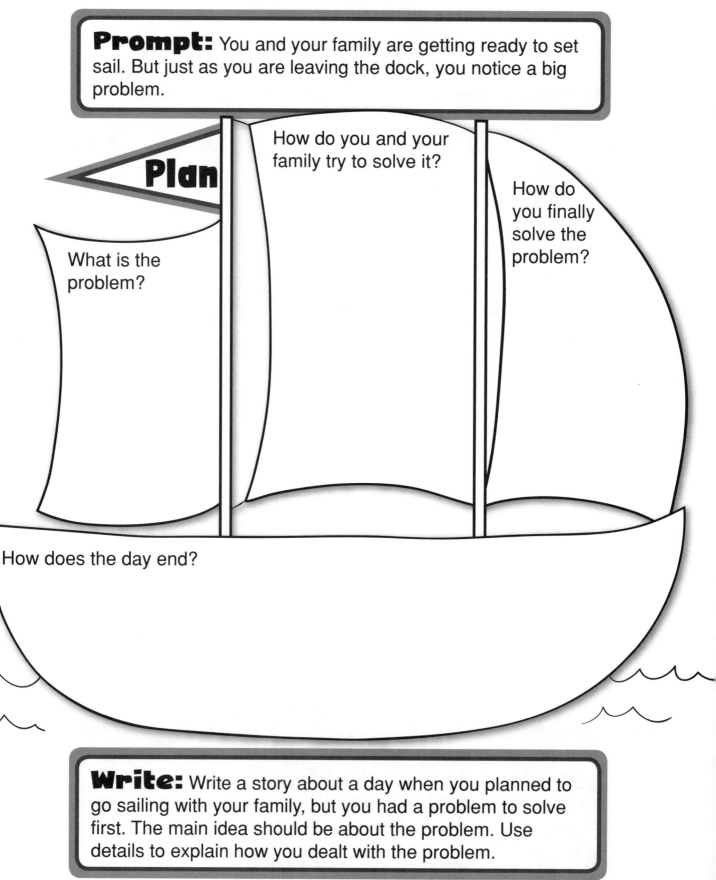

Prompt: You and your family are getting ready to set sail. But just as you are leaving the dock, you notice a big problem.

Plan

How do you and your family try to solve it?

How do you finally solve the problem?

What is the problem?

How does the day end?

Write: Write a story about a day when you planned to go sailing with your family, but you had a problem to solve first. The main idea should be about the problem. Use details to explain how you dealt with the problem.

Toy Talk

Prompt: You are in a toy store. Suddenly, one of the toys begins to talk to you!

Plan

Which toy talks to you?

What does it tell you?

Are you surprised by what the toy says? Why or why not?

What do you do with the toy?

Write: Write about talking with the toy.

A Super Friend

Prompt: Pretend that your best friend is a superhero with the power to hear things the average human cannot. During a field trip to the zoo, your superhero friend asks for your help.

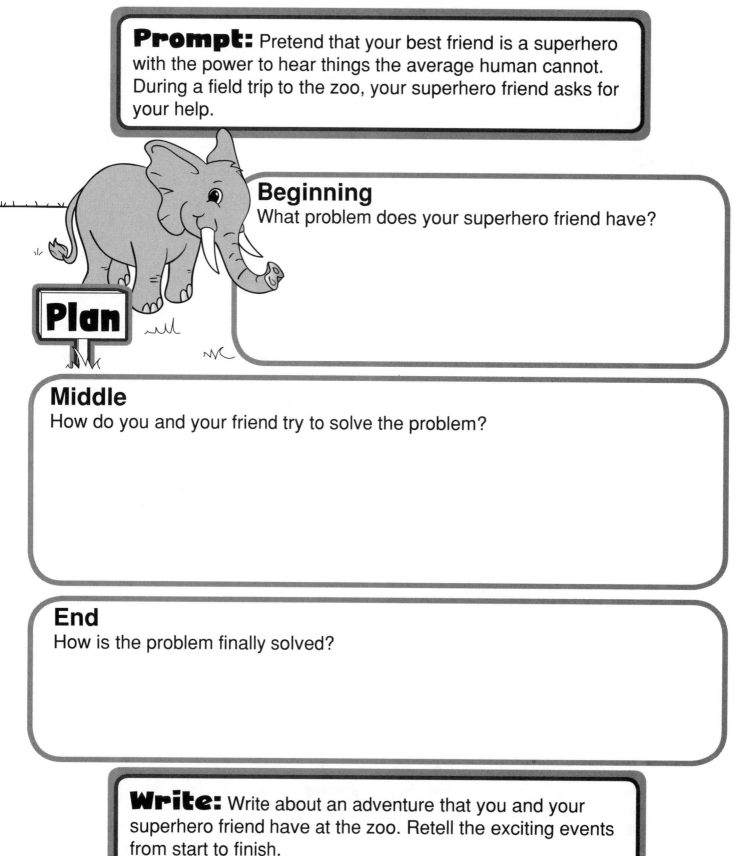

Plan

Beginning
What problem does your superhero friend have?

Middle
How do you and your friend try to solve the problem?

End
How is the problem finally solved?

Write: Write about an adventure that you and your superhero friend have at the zoo. Retell the exciting events from start to finish.

Leading the Pack

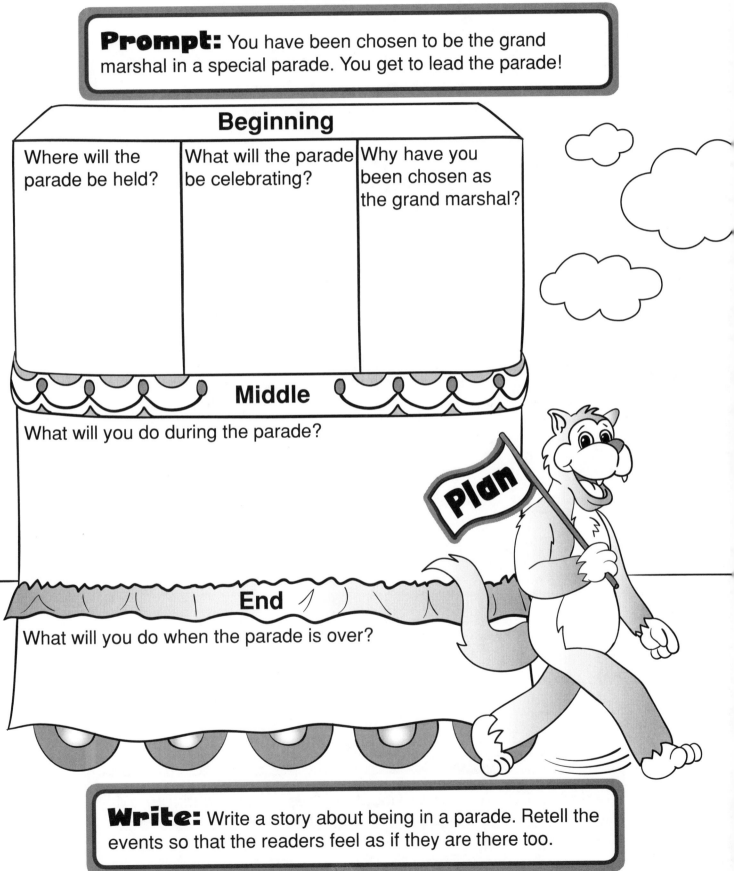

Prompt: You have been chosen to be the grand marshal in a special parade. You get to lead the parade!

Beginning

Where will the parade be held?

What will the parade be celebrating?

Why have you been chosen as the grand marshal?

Middle

What will you do during the parade?

End

What will you do when the parade is over?

Write: Write a story about being in a parade. Retell the events so that the readers feel as if they are there too.

Fishing for Answers

Prompt: One day you went fishing with some friends. It was a quiet day until you caught a very strange-looking fish.

Beginning
Where were you fishing?

What did the fish look like?

Middle
What did you do when you reeled in this strange-looking fish?

-
-
-

End
What did you finally do with the fish?

Write: Write a story about this special fishing trip. Retell the events from beginning to end. Use details to make the story interesting.

©The Mailbox® • *Prompt, Plan, Write!* • TEC61105

Picnic Problem

Prompt: You are going on a picnic with some friends. When you open your picnic basket, you see that something important is missing.

Plan

What is missing from your picnic basket?

What do you do to solve the problem?

First,

After that,

Then,

Finally,

Write: Write a story about going on a picnic. Tell what happens in the story in order.

Surprise!

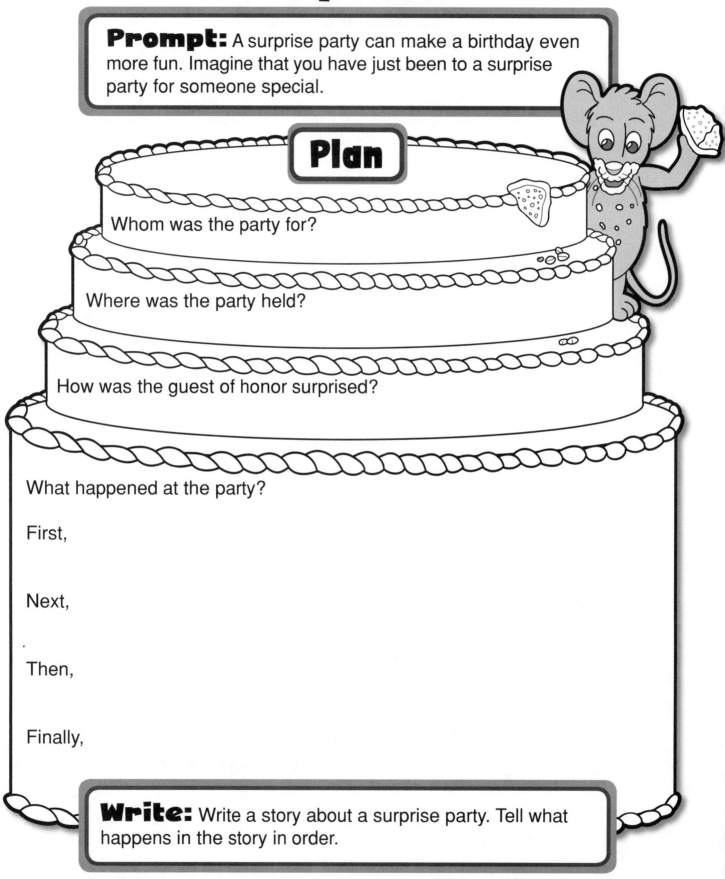

Prompt: A surprise party can make a birthday even more fun. Imagine that you have just been to a surprise party for someone special.

Plan

Whom was the party for?

Where was the party held?

How was the guest of honor surprised?

What happened at the party?

First,

Next,

Then,

Finally,

Write: Write a story about a surprise party. Tell what happens in the story in order.

Way Off Course

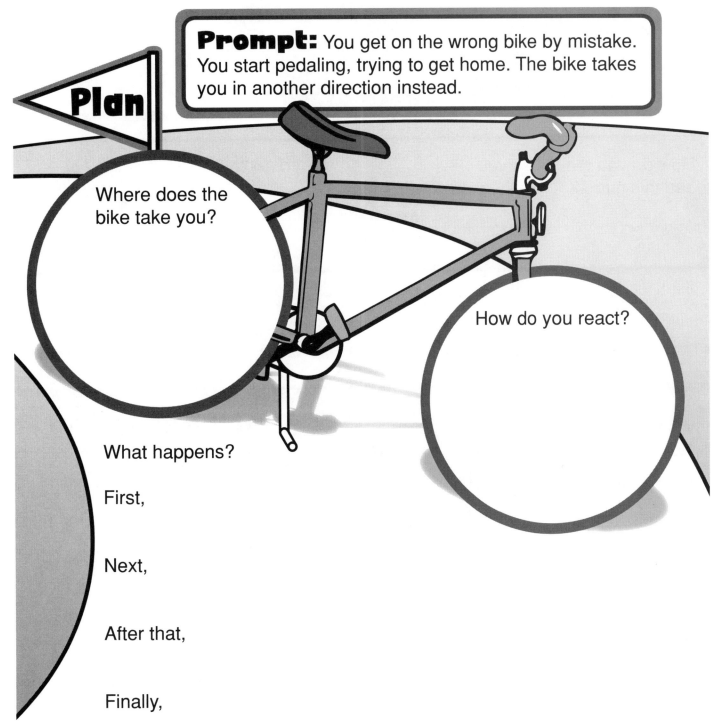

Plan

Prompt: You get on the wrong bike by mistake. You start pedaling, trying to get home. The bike takes you in another direction instead.

Where does the bike take you?

How do you react?

What happens?

First,

Next,

After that,

Finally,

Write: Write a story about a bike that takes you to a place you did not plan to go. Keep the reader involved by using strong details and by telling the story's events in order.

One More for Dinner

Prompt: It's dinnertime when the doorbell rings. You open the door and see an unexpected guest standing there. The guest is holding a covered dish and smiling.

How do you feel when you see this guest?

What does the guest look like?

Plan

What does the covered dish look like?

What do you smell coming from the covered dish?

Write: Write a story about a night you and your family spend with an unexpected dinner guest. Use details from your plan to make your story interesting.

On the Move

Prompt: Imagine that you are a library book. Think about the last trip you took out of the library.

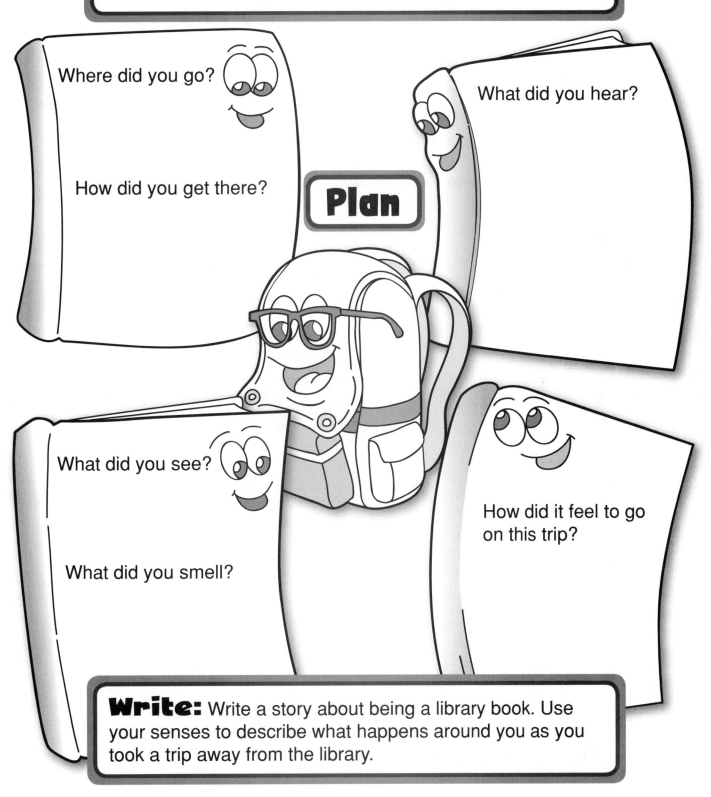

Where did you go?

How did you get there?

Plan

What did you hear?

What did you see?

What did you smell?

How did it feel to go on this trip?

Write: Write a story about being a library book. Use your senses to describe what happens around you as you took a trip away from the library.

Record-Setting Pizza

Prompt: You and your classmates are going to try to make the world's largest pizza.

Plan

Describe the toppings you will use on your pizza.

Describe the place where you will make the pizza.

Tell how long it will take to make the pizza.

Describe something that is as big as your pizza.

Write: Write a story about trying to make the world's largest pizza with your classmates. Use describing words in your story.

Crisp Changes

Prompt: Watching seasons change is interesting! Think about being outside on a fall day.

Plan

How does the air feel on a cool day?

What happens to the leaves on the trees during fall?

How do the leaves on the ground feel and sound during fall?

Write: Write about the fall day you are imagining. Describe the trees, the leaves, and the air.

Name_____

A Nibbler Nearby

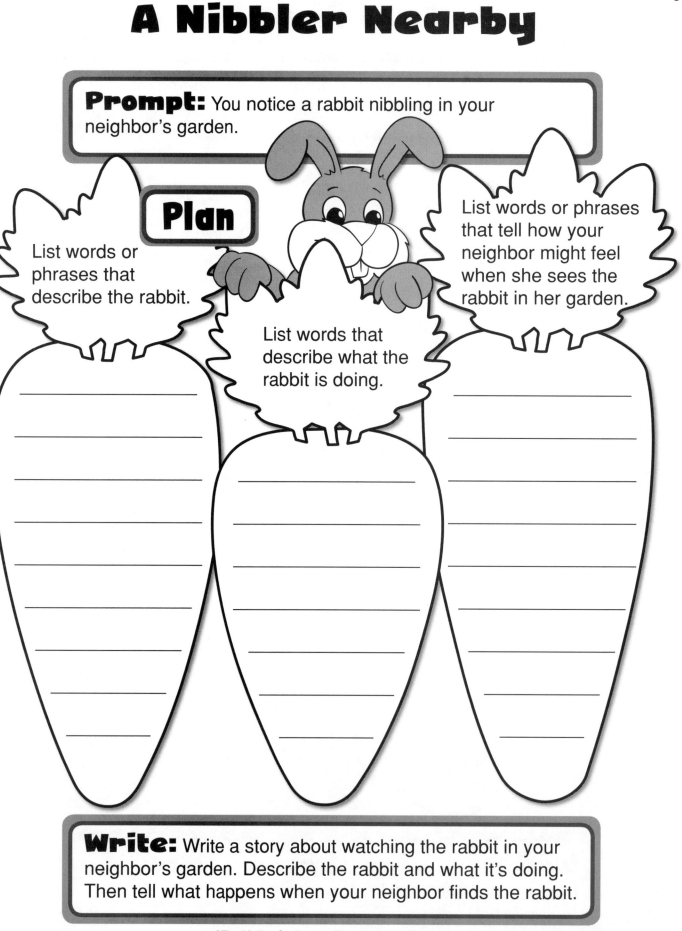

Prompt: You notice a rabbit nibbling in your neighbor's garden.

Plan

List words or phrases that describe the rabbit.

List words that describe what the rabbit is doing.

List words or phrases that tell how your neighbor might feel when she sees the rabbit in her garden.

Write: Write a story about watching the rabbit in your neighbor's garden. Describe the rabbit and what it's doing. Then tell what happens when your neighbor finds the rabbit.

©The Mailbox® • *Prompt, Plan, Write!* • TEC61105

In the Mountains

Prompt: Imagine that you have moved to a cabin in the mountains. A classmate from where you used to live wants to know about your new home.

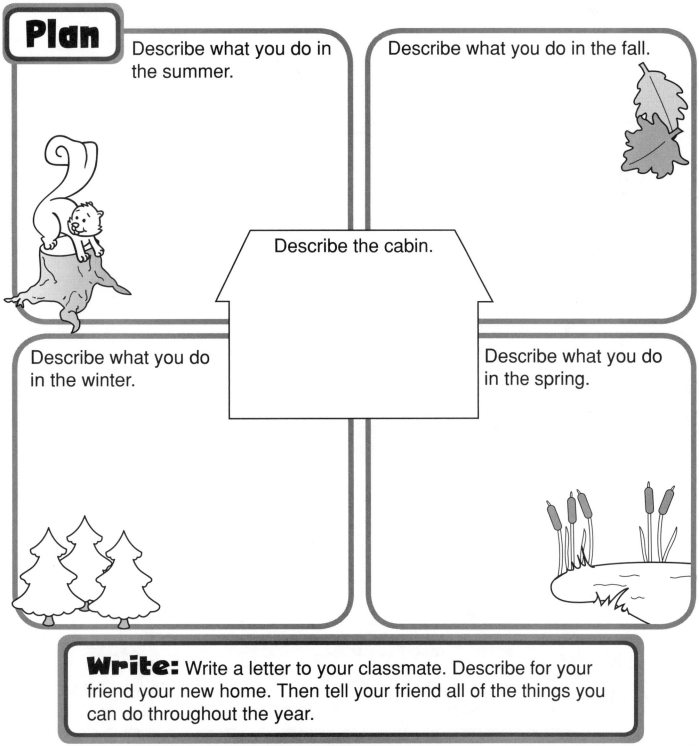

Plan

Describe what you do in the summer.

Describe what you do in the fall.

Describe the cabin.

Describe what you do in the winter.

Describe what you do in the spring.

Write: Write a letter to your classmate. Describe for your friend your new home. Then tell your friend all of the things you can do throughout the year.

A Wavy Ride

Prompt: Imagine that you are on a sailboat in the ocean.

Plan

Is it a good trip or a bad one?

What do you see?

What do you hear?

How do you feel on your trip?

Write: Write about your sailboat trip. Tell whether it is a good trip or a bad trip. Explain why.

What a Mess!

Prompt: Think about a time when you had to clean up a bedroom that was really messy.

Plan

What did you do first?

What kind of cleaning supplies did you use?

What was the hardest part of the cleanup? Why?

How long did it take to clean up the mess?

Write: Write about a time when you cleaned up a bedroom. Use details from your plan to tell how you cleaned the room.

Schoolwide Celebration

Prompt: Your school is having a contest to find a person other people admire. You know just the person to nominate!

Plan

Person's name _____

How do you know this person?

Beginning

Why do you admire this person?

What special things does this person do?

Middle

How does this person treat others?

What makes you sure this person should win the contest?

End

Write: Use your plan to write a nomination for the contest. Begin with a short introduction of the person. Then tell what makes this person special. End your nomination with a strong statement.

Feeling of Flight

Prompt: Imagine that you are riding in a hot-air balloon. What would your journey be like from liftoff to landing?

Plan

What does it feel like to…

…lift off the ground?

…climb into the air?

…soar high into the clouds?

…land gently back on the ground?

Write: Write a paragraph that describes how you feel during your flight. Describe each step of the journey, from the moment you launch into the air to the moment you land back on the ground.

In the Jungle

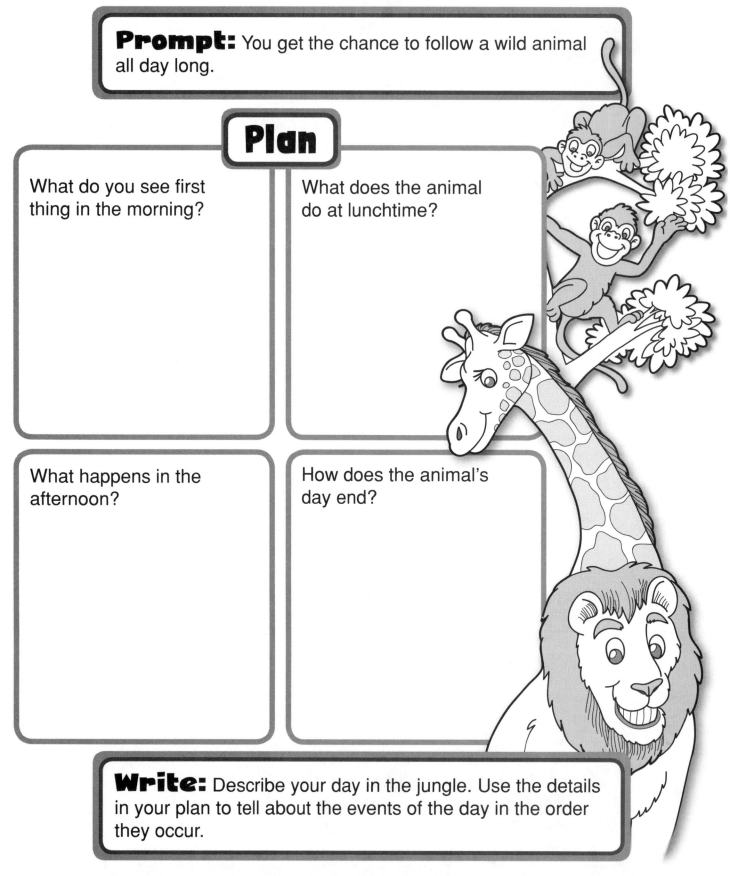

Prompt: You get the chance to follow a wild animal all day long.

Plan

What do you see first thing in the morning?

What does the animal do at lunchtime?

What happens in the afternoon?

How does the animal's day end?

Write: Describe your day in the jungle. Use the details in your plan to tell about the events of the day in the order they occur.

An Island of My Own

Prompt: Imagine that you live on an island in the middle of the ocean.

Plan

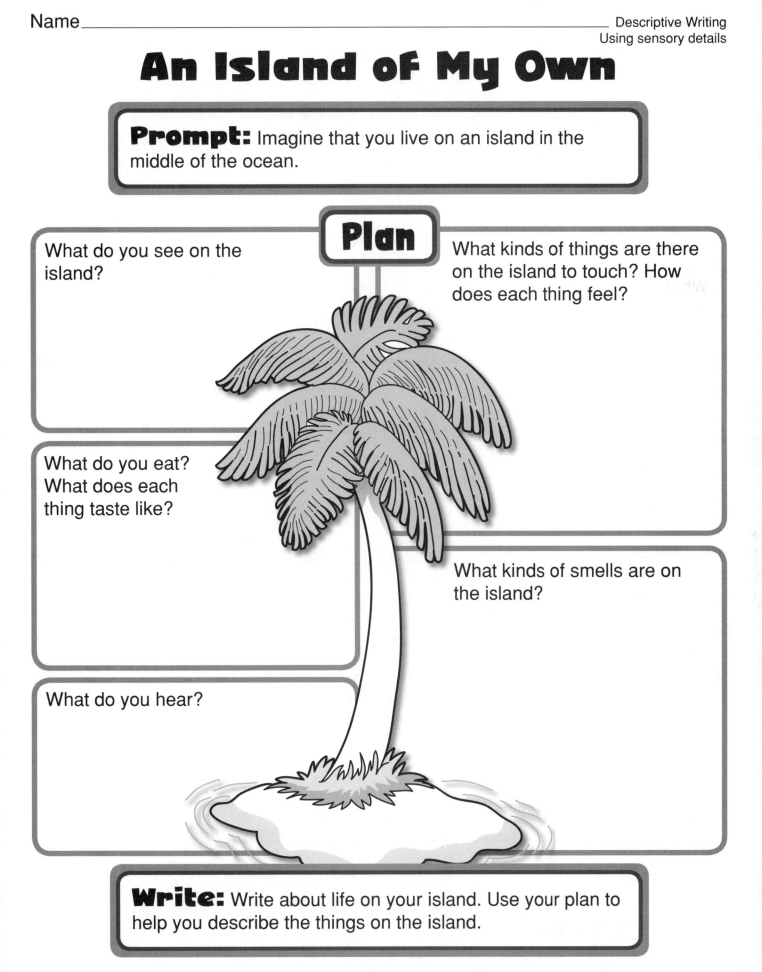

What do you see on the island?

What kinds of things are there on the island to touch? How does each thing feel?

What do you eat? What does each thing taste like?

What kinds of smells are on the island?

What do you hear?

Write: Write about life on your island. Use your plan to help you describe the things on the island.

Name_____

Best Wishes

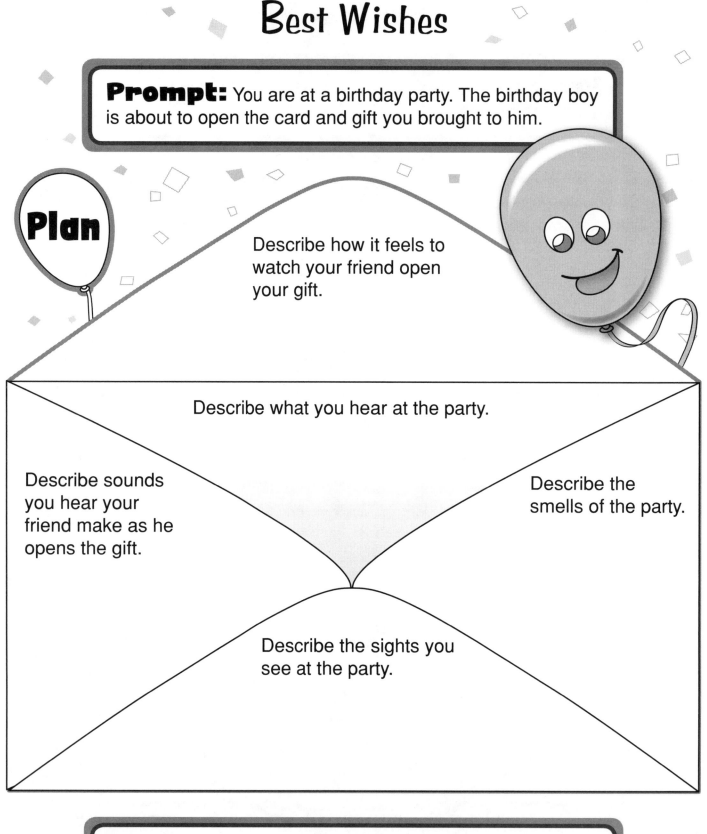

Prompt: You are at a birthday party. The birthday boy is about to open the card and gift you brought to him.

Plan

Describe how it feels to watch your friend open your gift.

Describe what you hear at the party.

Describe sounds you hear your friend make as he opens the gift.

Describe the smells of the party.

Describe the sights you see at the party.

Write: Write a story about the birthday party. Use details from your plan to make the story interesting.

©The Mailbox® • *Prompt, Plan, Write!* • TEC61105

Dream Room

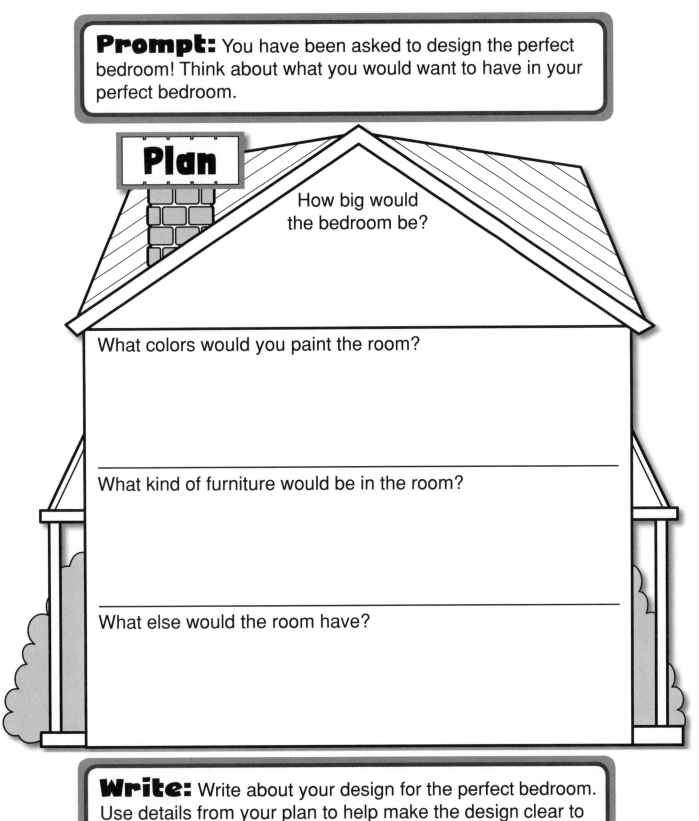

Prompt: You have been asked to design the perfect bedroom! Think about what you would want to have in your perfect bedroom.

Plan

How big would the bedroom be?

What colors would you paint the room?

_____

What kind of furniture would be in the room?

_____

What else would the room have?

Write: Write about your design for the perfect bedroom. Use details from your plan to help make the design clear to the reader.

Game On!

Prompt: Congratulations! You've been asked to invent a new video game. Think about what type of game you and your friends would love to play.

Plan

What type of game will you design?

What will you call your game?

What is the object of your game?

What colors will you use in your game?

What shapes and designs will you use in the game?

How do you want people to feel when they play your game?

Write: Write a description of the video game you want to design. Use adjectives that will make the reader want to play your game.

Deep-Sea Discovery

Prompt: You are scuba diving in the ocean. Suddenly, you find a treasure chest!

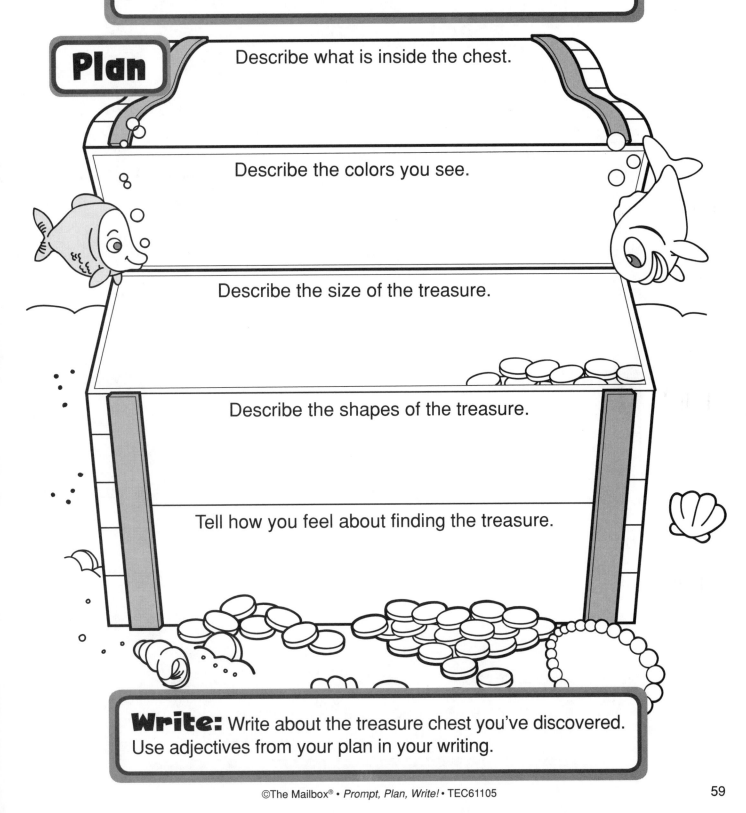

Plan

Describe what is inside the chest.

Describe the colors you see.

Describe the size of the treasure.

Describe the shapes of the treasure.

Tell how you feel about finding the treasure.

Write: Write about the treasure chest you've discovered. Use adjectives from your plan in your writing.

Take Me to the Zoo!

Prompt: You are a zookeeper. You have been asked to write a newspaper article about two of the animals in your zoo. Choose two zoo animals to write about.

Plan

Compare and contrast the two animals to each other. Use adjectives that compare to describe.

Their sizes:

Their looks:

Their actions:

Their speeds:

Their homes:

Write: Write a newspaper article about the two animals. Describe the animals using adjectives that compare.

Save the Park

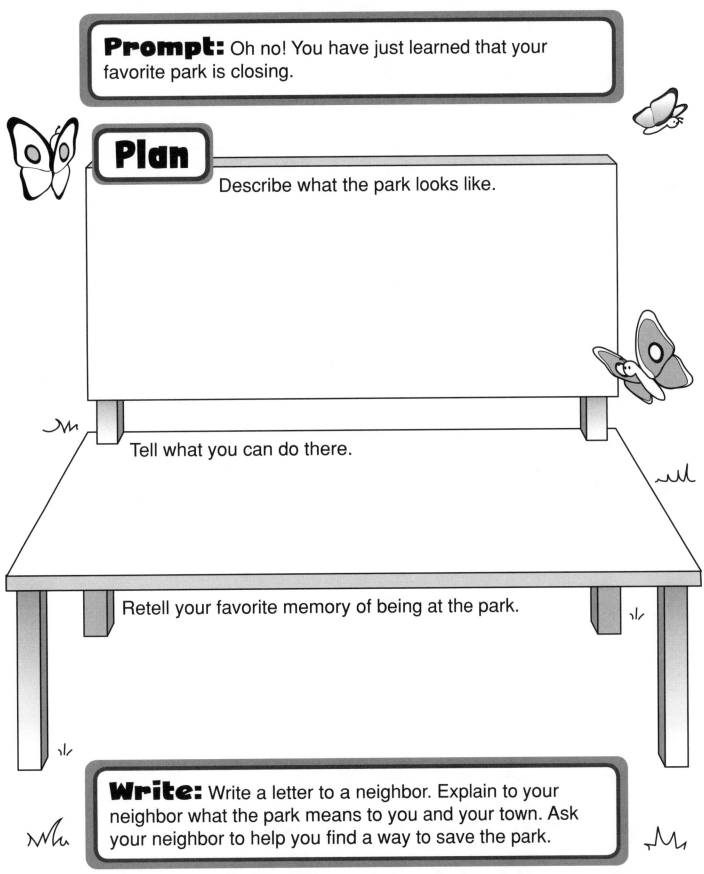

Prompt: Oh no! You have just learned that your favorite park is closing.

Plan

Describe what the park looks like.

Tell what you can do there.

Retell your favorite memory of being at the park.

Write: Write a letter to a neighbor. Explain to your neighbor what the park means to you and your town. Ask your neighbor to help you find a way to save the park.

Name_____

Gushing About a Gift

Prompt: It's not easy to find the right gift for someone. Imagine you receive the perfect gift.

Tell who gives you the gift and why it is given to you.

Describe the gift.

Plan

Tell why it is the perfect gift.

Describe how it feels to receive the gift.

Write: Write a thank-you letter to the person who gave you the gift.

©The Mailbox® • *Prompt, Plan, Write!* • TEC61105

Budding Friendship

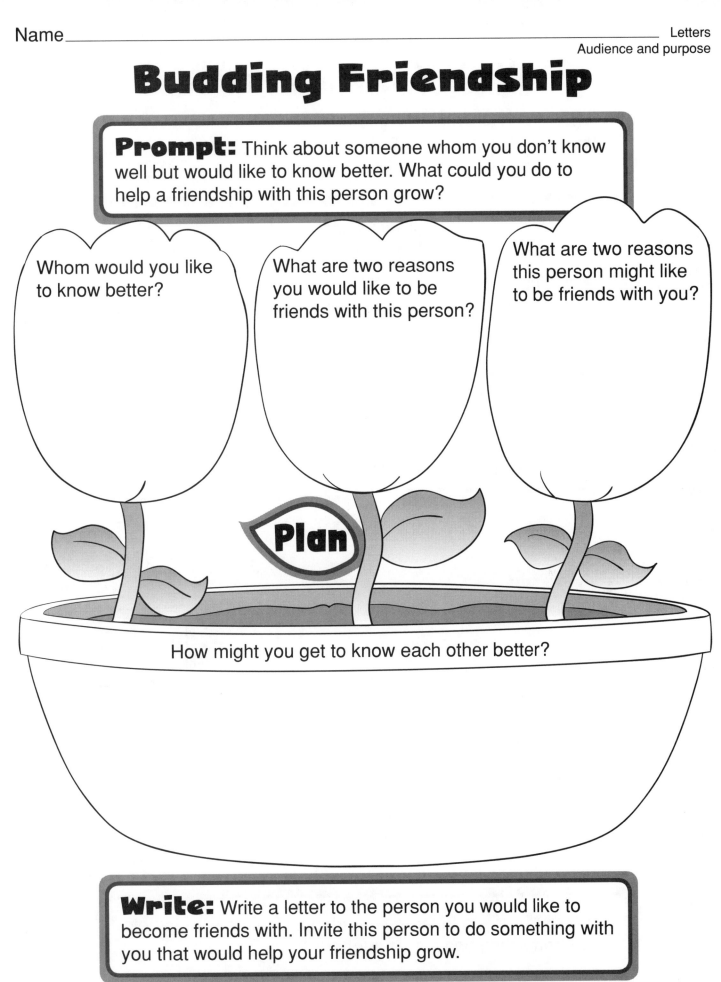

Prompt: Think about someone whom you don't know well but would like to know better. What could you do to help a friendship with this person grow?

Whom would you like to know better?

What are two reasons you would like to be friends with this person?

What are two reasons this person might like to be friends with you?

Plan

How might you get to know each other better?

Write: Write a letter to the person you would like to become friends with. Invite this person to do something with you that would help your friendship grow.

Wish You Were Here!

Prompt: You have been so busy that you have not seen one of your good friends all summer.

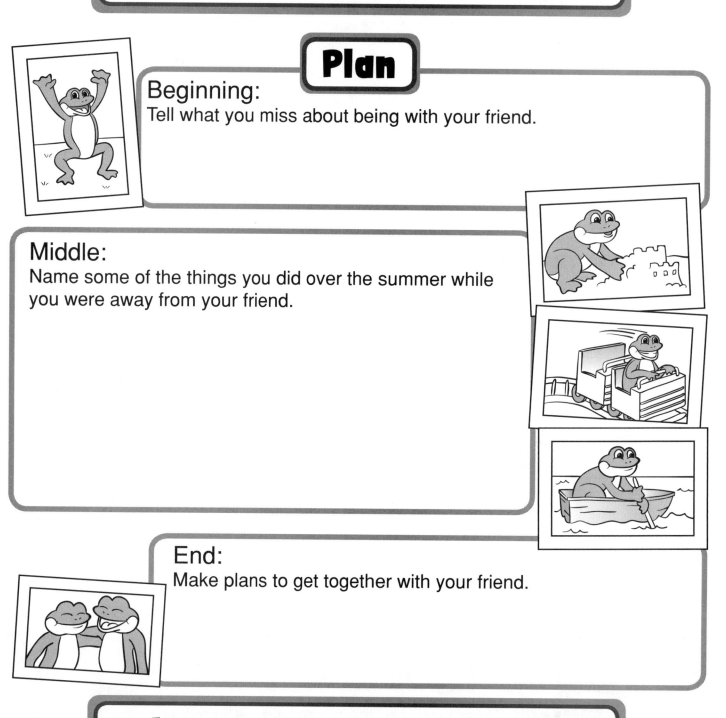

Plan

Beginning:
Tell what you miss about being with your friend.

Middle:
Name some of the things you did over the summer while you were away from your friend.

End:
Make plans to get together with your friend.

Write: Write a letter to your friend. Use the plan to help you organize the body of your letter.

A Stubborn Sidekick

Prompt: You are a young magician with a problem. Your rabbit will not come out of your hat! You need help.

Plan

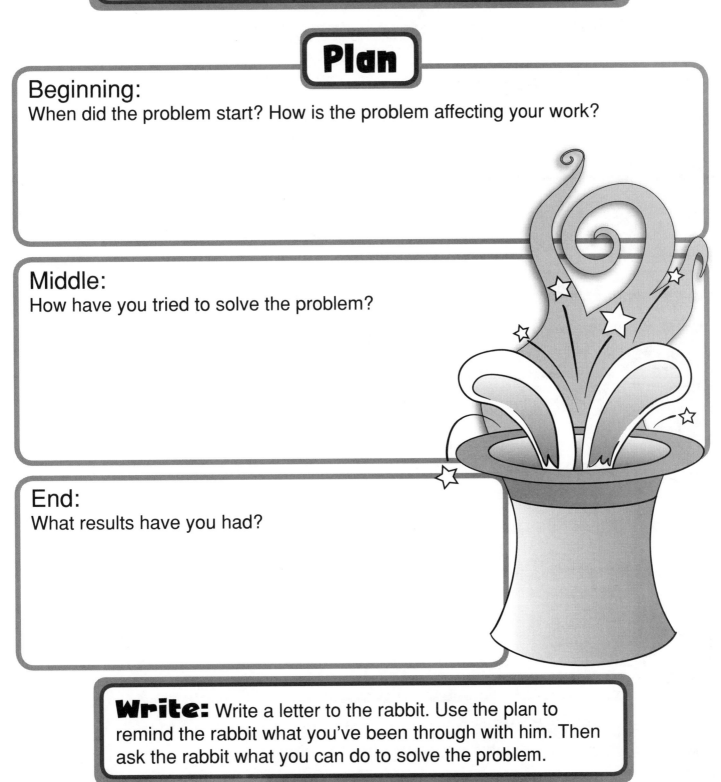

Beginning:
When did the problem start? How is the problem affecting your work?

Middle:
How have you tried to solve the problem?

End:
What results have you had?

Write: Write a letter to the rabbit. Use the plan to remind the rabbit what you've been through with him. Then ask the rabbit what you can do to solve the problem.

"Tanks" for Your Help!

Prompt: Pets need love and care. Your neighbor took care of your fish while you were on vacation.

Plan

Beginning:
List the things your neighbor did to help with your fish.

Middle:
Tell what you were able to do because your fish were being cared for.

End:
Name two or three things you can do to show your thanks.

Write: Write a thank-you letter to your neighbor. Use your plan to write your letter from beginning to end.

The Customer Is Always Right!

Prompt: Your new toy broke four days after you bought it. You want to get it replaced or fixed.

Plan

Tell what you bought and where you bought it.

Tell what you liked about the toy. Also tell how it broke.

Tell what you want to happen to solve the problem.

Write: Write a letter to the toy maker. Use your plan to help you explain your problem before you ask the toy maker to help you solve it.

Showered With Kindness

Prompt: A friend helped you in many ways when you were sick. Think about the things that he or she did to help you.

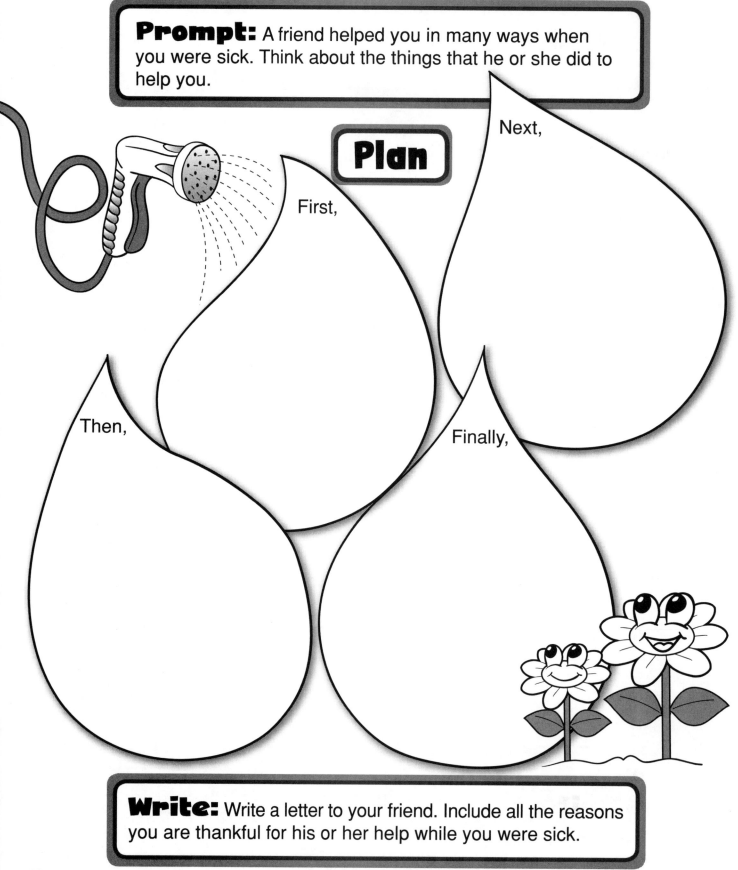

Plan

Next,

First,

Then,

Finally,

Write: Write a letter to your friend. Include all the reasons you are thankful for his or her help while you were sick.

Student Showcase

Prompt: You will perform in a school program, and you want a family member or friend to come and see you.

Plan

When and where will the program be held?

Why do you want this person to come to the show?

What will you do in the program?

What other acts will perform?

Write: Write a letter to your family member or friend. Invite this person to the program.

One Wish

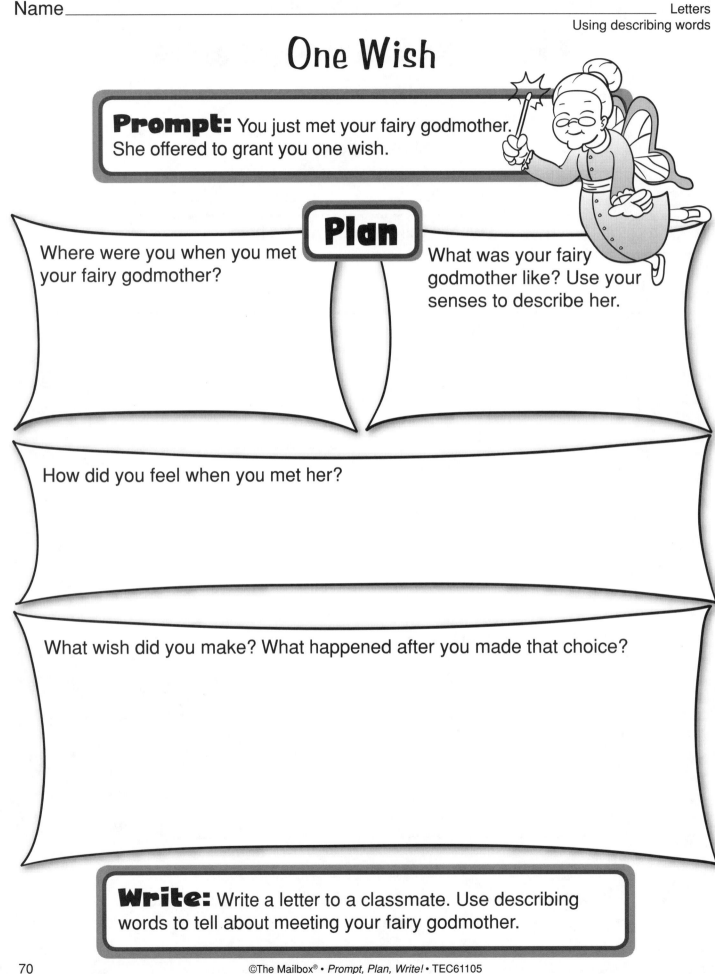

Prompt: You just met your fairy godmother.
She offered to grant you one wish.

Plan

Where were you when you met your fairy godmother?

What was your fairy godmother like? Use your senses to describe her.

How did you feel when you met her?

What wish did you make? What happened after you made that choice?

Write: Write a letter to a classmate. Use describing words to tell about meeting your fairy godmother.

Drop a Line

Prompt: You are a sea turtle stuck in a tangle of fishing line. A kind human helps you get free.

Plan

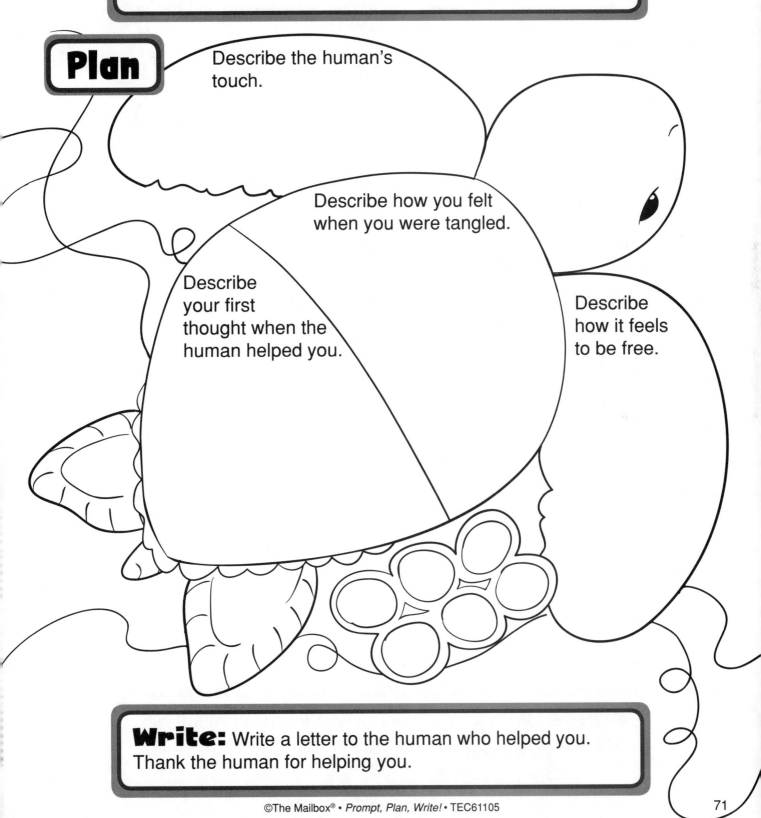

Describe the human's touch.

Describe how you felt when you were tangled.

Describe your first thought when the human helped you.

Describe how it feels to be free.

Write: Write a letter to the human who helped you. Thank the human for helping you.

Party Time

Prompt: You are planning a fiesta. Think about what this party will be like.

Plan

Name and describe the food and drinks you will serve.

Name and describe the games and activities you will have.

Describe the kind of music you will play.

Write: Write a letter to invite your friends to your fiesta. Use details to help your friends understand what your party will be like.

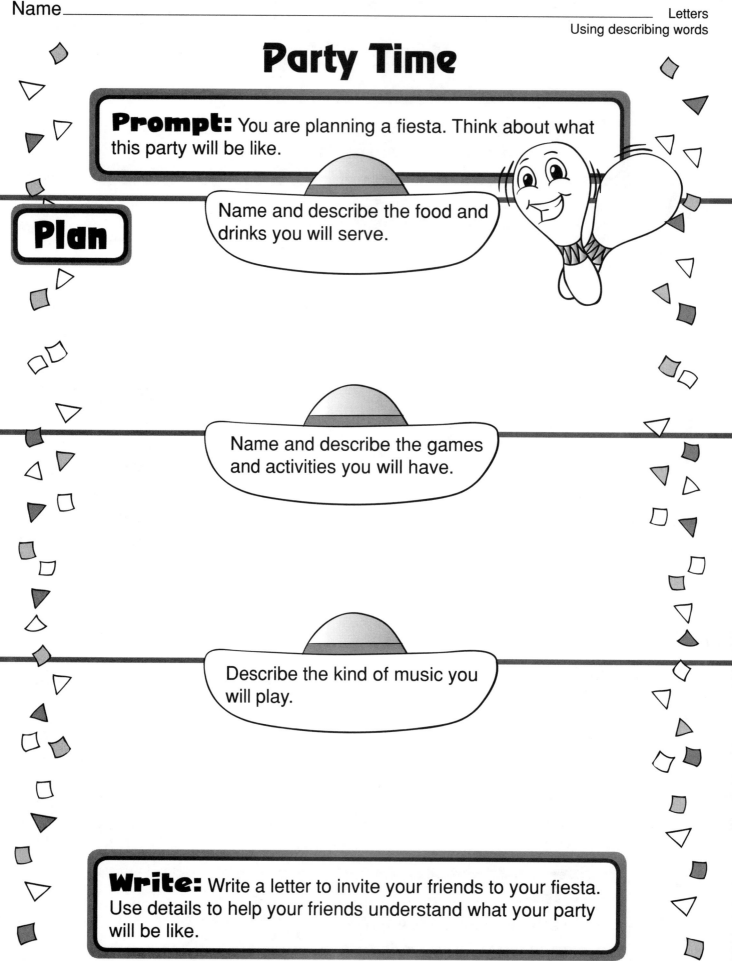

Trip Tips

Prompt: What do you need to do to get ready for a trip away from home?

Plan

What do you need to know about your trip before you go?	What will you need to do before you go?	What will you need to take with you on your trip?

Vacation **Guide**

Write: Write a paragraph explaining what you should do to get ready for your trip.

The Place to Be

Prompt: Think about what advice you would give a teacher to make his or her classroom lots of fun.

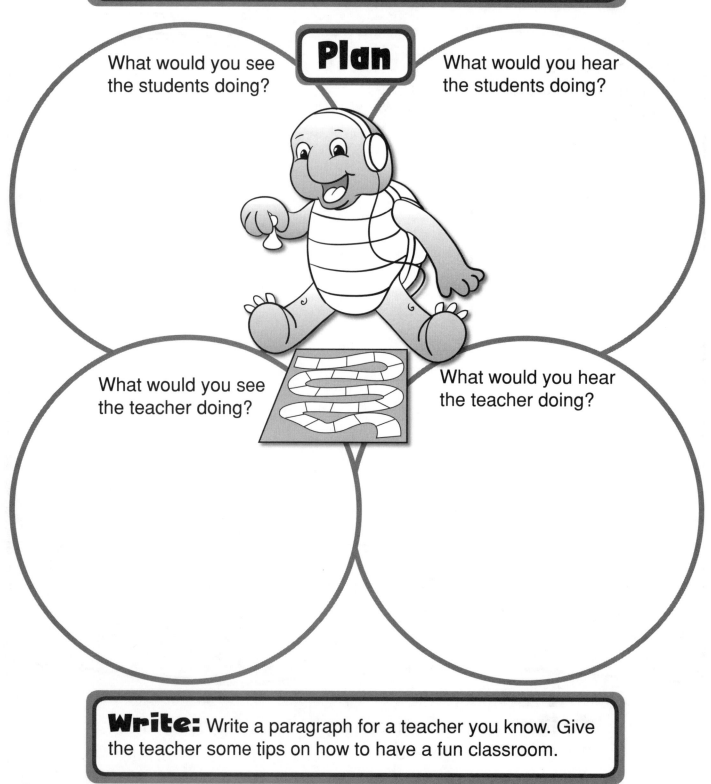

Plan

What would you see the students doing?

What would you hear the students doing?

What would you see the teacher doing?

What would you hear the teacher doing?

Write: Write a paragraph for a teacher you know. Give the teacher some tips on how to have a fun classroom.

Name _____

Escape Route

Prompt: What do you need to do during a fire drill?

Plan

What signal tells you that there is a fire drill?

What do you do before leaving the classroom?

What path do you take out of the school?

What happens when you get outside?

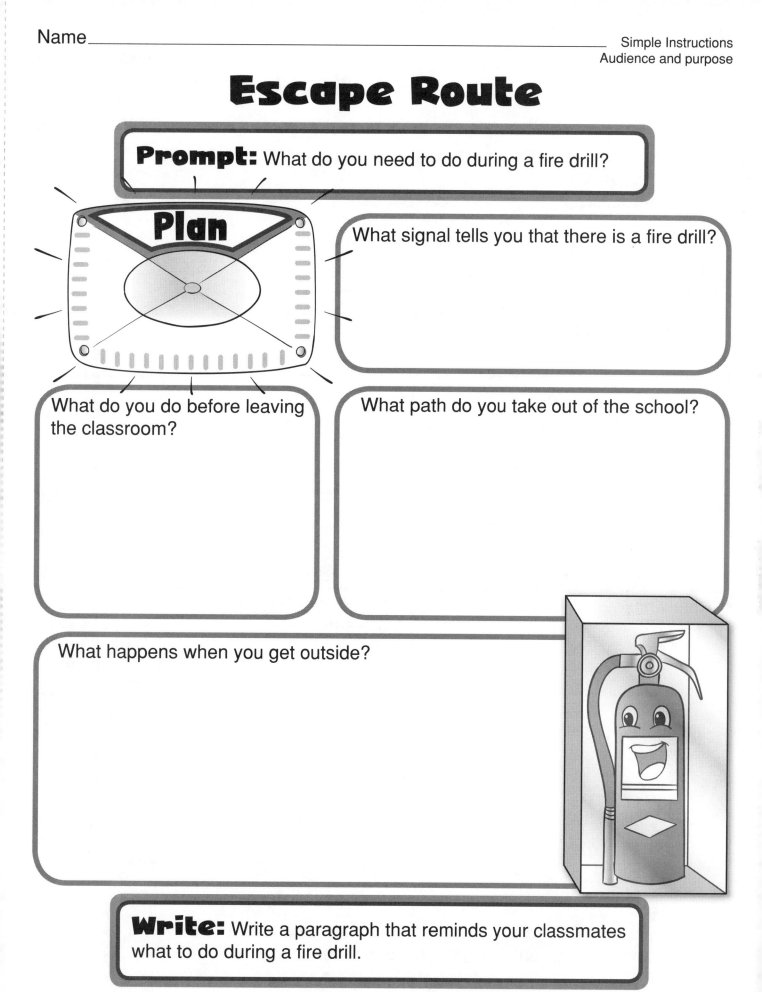

Write: Write a paragraph that reminds your classmates what to do during a fire drill.

That's a Wrap!

Prompt: Think about how you might wrap a special present.

Plan

What's the first step?	What's next?
Then what?	What kinds of final touches can you add?

Write: Write a paragraph to help a friend learn how to wrap a present. Put your ideas in order so your advice is clear.

Lunchtime Lesson

Prompt: How would you teach someone to eat a slice of pizza?

What should the eater do first?

What next?

Plan

Then what?

What is the last thing the eater should do?

Write: Write a set of instructions that teach someone how to eat a slice of pizza.

Name_____

Washed Away

Prompt: How do you wash your hands?

Plan

Step 1:

Step 2:

Step 3:

Step 4:

Step 5:

Write: Write instructions that tell other kids how to wash their hands.

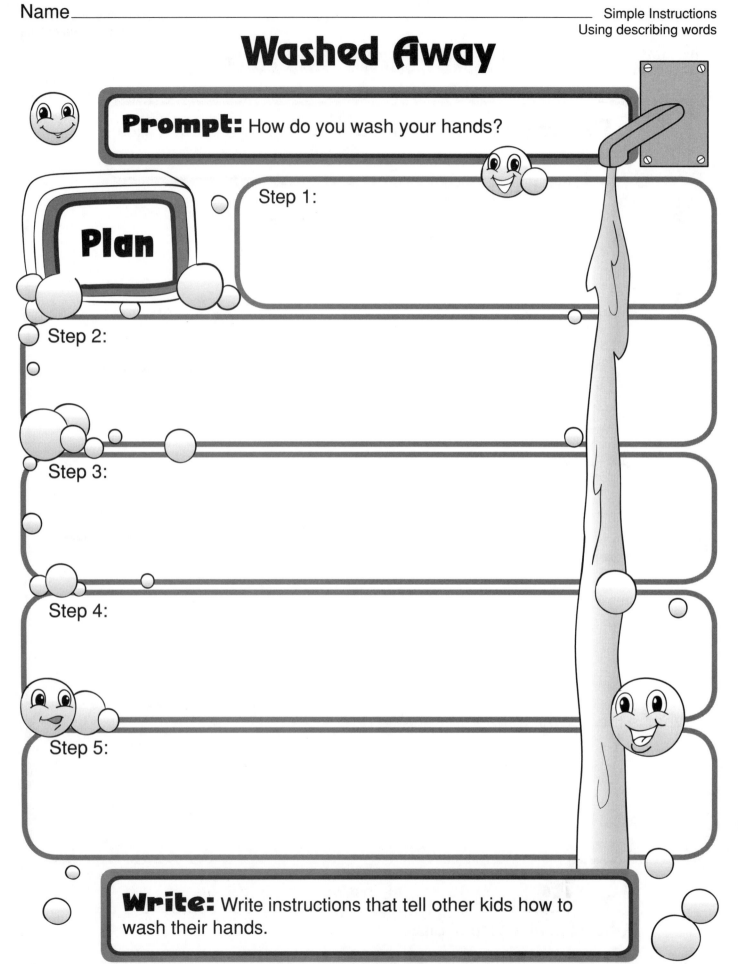

The Keys to Success

Prompt: What are the keys to doing homework successfully?

Plan

Describe the best place to do homework.

List the supplies you need.

How should a person act when he or she is doing homework?

Write: Write homework instructions for another student in your grade. Use descriptive words to share the keys for doing homework well.

A Clean Routine

Prompt: Think about the steps you take to brush your teeth.

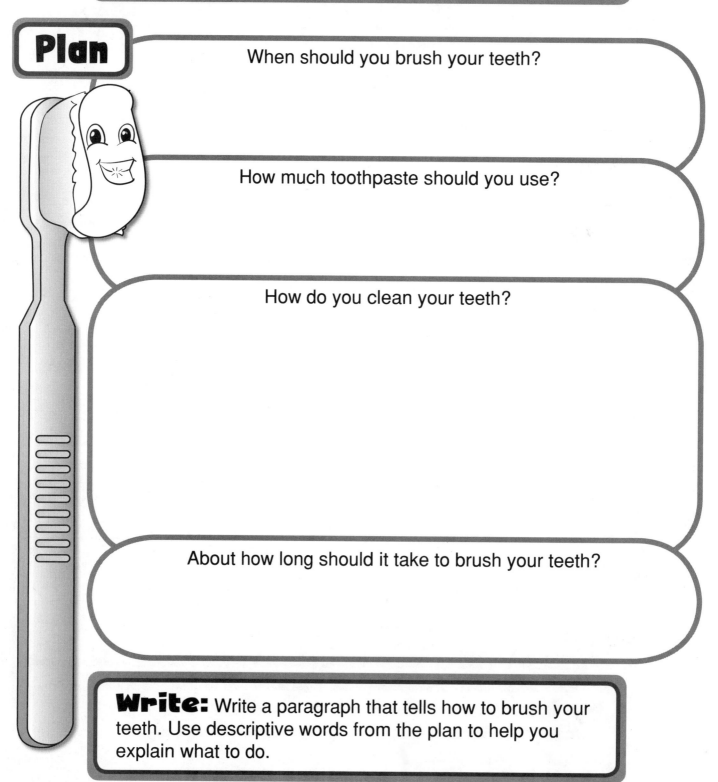

Plan

When should you brush your teeth?

How much toothpaste should you use?

How do you clean your teeth?

About how long should it take to brush your teeth?

Write: Write a paragraph that tells how to brush your teeth. Use descriptive words from the plan to help you explain what to do.